VOLUME

She

delighting in the examples
of the women of the Bible

Delight Thyself
DESIGN MINISTRIES

delightthyself.com

*To each of the Godly ladies
who have pointed me to His Word.*

Colossians 1:3-12

VOLUME 2

The Women of the Bible

She...

The series of *She* consists of four volumes, each focusing on the lives of 12 women of the Bible. Many of the women are familiar, some less spoken of, but each are applicable to our lives today.

The objective of this series is not an effort to reveal some new theory about the women, but simply to point us to the pages of the Word of God so that the Lord can speak to us as only He can. Ask Him to show you the Truths found within the testimonies of each of these women that He has preserved for us to read.

Symbols:

The leaves around a name signify the beginning of the study of a new woman.

SHE...
This shows us a quality that we can apply to ourselves, or seek to become.

SHE...
This denotes a fact about them as women during their time in history.

Read

A suggested passage for the context of the study.

Memorize

Verse(s) to help apply the characteristics of the woman.

Apply

A question or two to encourage you to dwell on what can be learned from the example of the woman of the Bible.

Anna

Read: Luke 2:36-38

Luke 2:36

"...she was of a great age..."

SHE WAS HUMBLE AND FAITHFUL.

Luke 2:36

"And there was one Anna, a _____, the daughter of Phanuel,

of the _____ of Aser: she was of a great age, and had lived

with an husband _____ years from her virginity;"

She believed in the prophecies that she had heard
for many years about the coming Messiah.

Luke 2:37

"And she was a widow of about _____ and four years,

which departed not from the temple, but _____ God

with fastings and _____ night and day."

SHE WAS OLD IN AGE, BUT YOUNG AT HEART.

SHE WAS DEVOTED TO SERVING GOD.

She patiently and faithfully watched for His coming.

Luke 2:38

"And she coming in that instant gave _____ likewise unto the Lord,

and _____ of him to all them

that looked for _____ in Jerusalem."

SHE WAS THE FIRST TO PROCLAIM JESUS AS CHRIST.

She spoke of the redemption found in Him
to many in Jerusalem.

After Mary and Joseph left the temple where Simeon blessed them
and declared that Jesus was for a sign,
she once again returned to faithfully fast and pray.

**But if was different this time...
her faith had become sight.**

SHE HAD SEEN THE LORD, AND WOULD SPEND
THE REST OF HER DAYS TELLING OF THE REDEMPTION HE OFFERS.

She...

ANNA SERVES AS AN EXAMPLE

OF TRUE FAITHFULNESS AND DETERMINATION

TO TELL OTHERS ABOUT

THE REDEMPTIVE WORK OF CHRIST.

Memorize:
2 Corinthians 9:15
"Thanks be unto God for his unspeakable gift."

Apply:
Who does Anna remind you of?

_____

_____

How old was she? Luke 2:37

_____

Notes

_____

_____

_____

_____

_____

_____

_____

_____

_____

_____

_____

_____

Eve

Eve

Genesis 2:23

"...she shall be called Woman..."

SHE WAS TAKEN OUT OF MAN.

Genesis 2:23

"And Adam said, This is now _____ of my bones, and _____ of my flesh: she shall be called Woman, because she was taken _____ of Man."

SHE WAS CREATED IN THE IMAGE OF GOD.

Genesis 1:27

"So God created man in his _____ image, in the image of God created he him; male and _____ created he them."

SHE WAS CALLED WOMAN.

SHE WAS CREATED WITH PURPOSE.

Genesis 2:18

"And the LORD God said, It is not _____ that the man should be alone; I will make him an _____ _____ for him."

She was formed not out of the dust of the ground,
but from the rib of her husband, the only woman never born.

Genesis 2:21-22

"And the LORD God caused a deep _____ to fall upon Adam, and he slept: and he took one of his ribs, and closed up the _____ instead thereof; And the _____, which the LORD God had taken from man, made he a _____, and brought her unto the man."

**She was the help meet of the man,
for she was not taken from his feet, but his side.**

Genesis 1:28

"And God _____ them, and God said unto them,

Be _____, and multiply, and replenish the earth..."

She...

THE FIRST WOMAN SERVES AS AN EXAMPLE THAT GOD CREATES EACH WOMAN WITH PURPOSE AND HAS A UNIQUE PLAN FOR HER LIFE.

Memorize:
Genesis 2:24
*"Therefore shall a man leave his father and his mother,
and shall cleave unto his wife: and they shall be one flesh."*

Apply:
Why do you think God created the Woman from the rib of Adam?

_____

_____

_____

Genesis 3:6

"...she took of the fruit thereof..."

SHE DESIRED WHAT THE TREE HAD TO OFFER.

**Sin will take you farther than you want to go,
and cost you more than you want to pay.**

Genesis 3:1

"Now the _____ was more subtil than any beast of the field

which the LORD _____ had made. And he said unto the woman,

Yea, hath God _____, Ye shall not eat of every tree of the garden?"

The serpent subtly convinced her what God had said was not true.
He has been deceiving people against the Word of God since the beginning.

Genesis 2:16-17

"And the LORD God commanded the man, saying, Of every tree of the garden thou

mayest _____ eat: But of the tree of the _____ of good and evil,

thou shalt not eat of it: for in the day that thou eatest thereof thou shalt surely die."

God had told Adam this, yet the woman added to the Word of God
by saying that He told them not even to touch it.

SHE WAS DECEIVED.

Genesis 3:4-5

"And the serpent said unto the woman, Ye shall _____ surely die: For God doth

know that in the day ye eat thereof, then your _____ shall be opened,

and ye shall be as gods, _____ good and evil."

SHE HAD A CHOICE TO MAKE.

Genesis 3:6

"And when the woman saw that the tree was _____ for food,

and that it was _____ to the eyes, and a tree to be desired

to make one _____, she took of the fruit thereof, and did _____,

and gave also unto her _____ with her; and he did _____."

SHE GAVE IT TO HER HUSBAND, AND HE ATE TOO.
And the rest is history.

Romans 5:12

"Wherefore, as by one man _____ entered into the world, and _____ by sin;

and so death passed upon _____ men, for that all have _____:"

She was not given her name until after she took of the fruit.

Genesis 3:20

"And Adam called his wife's name Eve; because she was the _____ of all living."

She was the first mother. She was the first to see her child die.
She was given another child after her great loss.

She...

EVE ALSO SERVES AS AN EXAMPLE THAT EVEN WHEN WE FALL, GOD STILL HAS A PURPOSE FOR US.

**He can use us despite our sin,
and fulfill His will through us if we will simply yield to Him.**

Memorize:
Romans 6:23
"For the wages of sin is death; but the gift of God is eternal life through Jesus Christ our Lord."

Apply:

What has Eve taught you? _____

Notes

_____

_____

_____

_____

_____

_____

_____

_____

_____

_____

_____

Hannah

Hannah

1 Samuel 1:10

"...she was in bitterness of soul..."

SHE HAD NO CHILDREN.

1 Samuel 1:4-5

"And when the time was that _____ offered, he gave to Peninnah his wife,

and to all her sons and her daughters, portions:

But unto Hannah he gave a _____ portion; for he loved Hannah:

but the LORD had _____ up her womb."

**The Lord had shut up her womb, and her adversary
used the thing most near and dear to her heart to provoke her.**

1 Samuel 1:6

"And her adversary also provoked her _____, for to make her fret,

because the _____ had shut up her womb."

Our enemy knows how to get our attention.

He knows how to distract, discourage, and even depress us,
in an effort to defeat us before we see what God has in store.

1 Samuel 1:7

"And as he did so _____ by year, when she went up

to the house of the LORD, so she provoked her;

therefore she _____, and did not eat."

SHE WAS PERSISENTLY PROVOKED BY HER ADVERSARY.

So much so that she cried away her appetite.

1 Samuel 1:8

"Then said Elkanah her husband to her, Hannah, why _____ thou?

and why eatest thou not? and why is thy _____ grieved?

am not I better to thee than ten sons?"

Her heart was grieved because she longed for something more.

SHE CHOSE TO USE THE BITTERNESS INSIDE TO CAUSE HER TO PRAY UNTO THE LORD.

1 Samuel 1:10

"And she was in bitterness of soul,

and _____ unto the LORD, and wept sore."

She...

HANNAH SERVES AS AN EXAMPLE THAT WHEN OUR HEART HURTS, THE EARS OF THE LORD ARE OPEN TO OUR CRY.

Memorize:
Psalm 18:6
*"In my distress I called upon the LORD,
and cried unto my God: he heard my voice out of his temple,
and my cry came before him, even into his ears."*

Apply:
Have you ever been provoked like Hannah was? What did the Lord teach you?

_____

_____

_____

1 Samuel 1:11

"...she vowed a vow..."

SHE PROMISED THE LORD.

1 Samuel 1:11

"And she vowed a vow, and said, O LORD of hosts, if thou wilt indeed look on the

_____ of thine handmaid, and _____ me,

and not forget thine handmaid, but wilt give unto thine handmaid a man child,

then I will _____ him unto the LORD all the _____ of his life,

and there shall no razor come upon his head."

SHE VOWED WHAT SHE WOULD DO
IF HE SUPPLIED THE DESIRE OF HER HEART.

She told the Lord that if He gave her a man child,
she would give him back to Him.

SHE WEPT AND PRAYED UNTO THE LORD.

Eli the priest was watching as she prayed,
and wrongfully assumed she was drunk because of her actions.

1 Samuel 1:12-14

"And it came to pass, as she continued _____ before the LORD,

that Eli marked her mouth. Now Hannah, she _____ in her heart;

only her lips moved, but her voice was _____ heard:

therefore Eli thought she had been _____. And Eli said unto her,

How long wilt thou be drunken? put away thy wine from thee."

She immediately corrected him, and admitted her true condition.

1 Samuel 1:15

"And Hannah answered and said, _____, my lord,

I am a woman of a _____ spirit: I have drunk neither wine

nor strong drink, but have _____ out my soul before the LORD."

She pleaded with the Lord that He would give her the desire of her heart.

She...

Hannah also serves as an example of how serious it is to make a vow to God.

Ecclesiastes 5:4-5

"When thou vowest a vow unto God, defer not to _____ it;

for he hath no pleasure in fools: _____ that which thou hast vowed.

Better is it that thou shouldest _____ vow,

than that thou shouldest _____ and not pay."

Memorize:
Romans 11:29
"For the gifts and calling of God are without repentance."

Apply:
What are you asking the Lord to do for you? Have you ever made a vow to Him?

_____

_____

1 Samuel 1:20

"...she bare a son, and called his name Samuel..."

SHE PRAYED SINCERELY.

SHE VOWED TO GIVE HIM BACK TO THE LORD.

Eli prophesied that He would grant that request.

1 Samuel 1:17

"Then Eli answered and said, Go in _____: and the God of Israel

grant thee thy petition that thou hast _____ of him."

SHE BELIEVED THAT GOD WAS ABLE.

Eli encouraged her to wait patiently in faith.
Her faith changed her countenance.

1 Samuel 1:18

"And she said, Let thine handmaid find _____ in thy sight. So the woman

went her way, and did eat, and her countenance was _____ more sad."

SHE HAD PEACE
THAT GOD WOULD PROVIDE IN HIS TIME.

SHE BEGAN TO WORSHIP THE LORD FOR WHAT HE WOULD DO.

1 Samuel 1:19

"And they rose up in the morning early, and _____ before the LORD,

and returned, and came to their house to Ramah: and Elkanah _____ Hannah

his wife; and the LORD _____ her."

The Lord remembered her prayers, her affliction, and her vow.
Her sincerity and faith allowed the Lord to do a work in and through her.

1 Samuel 1:20

"Wherefore it came to pass, when the time was _____ about after Hannah

had conceived, that she bare a son, and called his name Samuel, saying,

Because I have _____ him of the LORD."

The Lord gave her a son just as she asked.

**Every time she spoke his name she remembered
that he was the answer to her prayers.**

After he was weaned, she brought Samuel to Eli at the temple,
just as she had promised the Lord she would do.

She honored her word to the Lord, just as He honors His.

1 Samuel 1:27-28

"For this child I _____; and the LORD hath given me my petition which I

asked of him: Therefore also I have _____ him to the LORD; as long as he

liveth he shall be lent to the LORD. And he _____ the LORD there."

She...

HANNAH ALSO SERVES AS AN EXAMPLE THAT
GOD WILL GIVE US THE DESIRES OF OUR HEART,
IF WE WILL FIRST DELIGHT IN HIM.

Memorize:
Psalm 37:4-5
"Delight thyself also in the LORD;
and he shall give thee the desires of thine heart.
Commit thy way unto the LORD; trust also in him;
and he shall bring it to pass."

Apply:
What is the desire of your heart today? Delight and trust in Him to bring it to pass.

Notes

_____

_____

_____

_____

_____

_____

_____

_____

_____

_____

_____

Jochebed

Jochebed

Exodus 2:2

"...she hid him three months."

She had a beautiful baby boy.

Exodus 2:2

"And the woman conceived, and bare a _____: and when she saw him that he

was a _____ child, she hid him three months."

She knew there was something different about him, and was determined to fight for his life.

Acts 7:20

"In which time Moses was born, and was _____ fair,

and nourished up in his father's house _____ months:"

She kept him hidden inside the house as long as she could to protect him
from the execution of the law that all male Hebrew children were to be murdered.

Exodus 2:3

"And when she could not longer _____ him, she took for him an _____

of bulrushes, and daubed it with slime and with _____, and put the child

therein; and she _____ it in the flags by the river's brink."

She carefully prepared an ark of bulrushes,
covered it with slime and pitch,
and placed him inside.

The same pitch that Noah used on his Ark of Salvation.

She refused to leave him unattended.

She left his sister to watch what would befall her young brother.
She watched Pharaoh's Daughter come and find Moses,
and then offered to find her a Hebrew nurse to tend to the baby's needs.

Exodus 2:8-9

"And Pharaoh's daughter said to her, _____. And the maid went

and called the child's _____. And Pharaoh's daughter said unto her,

Take this child away, and nurse it for me, and I will _____ thee thy wages.

And the woman took the child, and _____ it."

Where God guides, He provides.

She not only saved the life of her goodly son,
she got paid to feed her own son until he was weaned.

SHE HAD FAITH GOD WOULD PROTECT HER SON.

When she placed Moses in the river that day,
she had faith that he would not only survive, but also thrive.
All three of Jochebed's children were devoted to serve the Lord.

They must have learned this from their mother.

JOCHEBED SERVES AS AN EXAMPLE THAT GOD CAN USE THE MOST UNIQUE SITUATIONS TO PROTECT HIS CHILDREN AND HIS PLAN FOR THEIR LIVES.

Her name means, "Glory to Jehovah".
She was the first person within the Scriptures
to have their name compounded with Jehovah.

Memorize:
Proverbs 22:6
*"Train up a child in the way he should go:
and when he is old, he will not depart from it."*

Apply:
What have you placed in your basket in faith that God would intervene?

_____

Notes

_____

_____

_____

_____

_____

_____

_____

_____

_____

_____

_____

Mary Magdalene

Mary Magdalene

Mark 16:10

"...she went and told them..."

SHE WATCHED HIM DIE ON THE CROSS.
SHE SAW HIS BODY BURIED INSIDE THE TOMB.
SHE WAS THE FIRST TO SEE JESUS AFTER HE HAD RISEN.

Mark 16:9

"Now when Jesus was risen _____ the first day of the week, he appeared

first to Mary Magdalene, out of whom he had cast _____ devils."

He told her to go and tell the Good News to the others.

John 20:17

"Jesus saith unto her, _____ me not; for I am not yet ascended to my Father:

but _____ to my _____, and say unto them, I ascend unto my Father,

and _____ Father; and to my God, and _____ God."

SHE OBEYED HIM.

Mark 16:10

"And she went and told them that had been _____ him,

as they _____ and wept."

John 20:18

"Mary Magdalene came and told the _____ that she had seen the Lord,

and that he had _____ these things unto her."

SHE SHARED THE GOSPEL.

SHE TOLD THE DISCIPLES THAT HE WAS ALIVE, BUT THEY DID NOT BELIEVE HER.

Mark 16:11

"And they, when they had _____ that he was alive,

and had been _____ of her, believed not."

They had to see for themselves before they would believe the Truth.
May we never let the response of others prevent us from sharing the Gospel.

She...

MARY MAGDALENE SERVES AS AN EXAMPLE OF HOW WE SHOULD OBEY CHRIST BY TELLING OTHERS ABOUT HIM.

Memorize:
Mark 16:15
"And he said unto them, *Go ye into all the world, and preach the gospel to every creature.***"**

Apply:
How does Mary Magdalene inspire you to reach others?

_____

_____

_____

John 20:11

"...she stooped down, and looked into the sepulchre..."

SHE SAW THE STONE ROLLED AWAY.

John 20:1

"The first _____ of the week cometh Mary Magdalene early,

when it was yet _____, unto the sepulchre,

and seeth the _____ taken away from the sepulchre."

SHE RAN IN FEAR TO TELL SIMON PETER AND JOHN THAT THE BODY OF JESUS WAS MISSING.

John 20:2

"Then she _____, and cometh to Simon Peter, and to the other disciple,

whom Jesus _____, and saith unto them, They have taken _____ the

Lord out of the sepulchre, and we know not _____ they have laid him."

Fear can cause us to do things we would never dream of otherwise.

SHE FORGOT.

Mark 9:31

"For he taught his disciples, and said unto them, The _____ of man is delivered

into the hands of men, and they shall _____him; and after that he is killed,

he shall rise the _____ day."

Perhaps out of shock, but still...she forgot.

SHE NEGLECTED TO REMEMBER WHAT JESUS HAD SAID WOULD HAPPEN.

SHE SAW JESUS,
BUT DID NOT KNOW IT WAS HIM AT FIRST.

She thought He was a gardener, until He said just one word.

John 20:16

"Jesus saith unto her, _____. She turned herself,

and saith unto him, Rabboni; which is to say, Master."

He knew her name, just as He knows ours.

She...

MARY MAGDALENE ALSO SERVES AS AN EXAMPLE OF THE FEAR THAT CAN CONSUME US WHEN WE FORGET WHAT THE WORD OF GOD SAYS.

Memorize:
John 14:1
"Let not your heart be troubled: ye believe in God, believe also in me."

Apply:
What does Mary Magdalene's reaction remind you of in your own life?

_____

_____

_____

Notes

_____

_____

_____

_____

_____

_____

_____

_____

_____

_____

_____

Naomi

Naomi

Ruth 1:6

"...she arose with her daughters in law..."

SHE AND HER HUSBAND FLED FROM THEIR HOME INSTEAD OF TRUSTING GOD TO PROVIDE.

They went to sojourn in Moab due to the famine in Bethlehem.

Ruth 1:3

"And Elimelech Naomi's husband _____; and she was left,

and her _____ sons."

Just three verses into the Book of Ruth,
we see Naomi's bliss depart with the death of her husband, Elimelech.

Her sons married in that foreign land of Moab,
giving her two daughters in law.
Jewish law forbade marriage outside of the nation of Israel.

Ruth 1:4

"And they took them _____ of the women of Moab;

the name of the one was _____, and the name of the other Ruth:

and they dwelled there about _____ years."

SHE DWELT IN THE LAND OF MOAB FOR AT LEAST 10 YEARS.

Though there was plenty to eat, she ended up feeling empty inside.

Ruth 1:5

"And Mahlon and Chilion _____ also both of them;

and the woman was _____ of her two sons and her husband."

After her great loss, she received word that the famine was over in Bethlehem.
The Lord was once again providing within the House of Bread.

Ruth 1:6

"Then she arose with her daughters in law,

that she might _____ from

the country of Moab: for she had _____ in the country of Moab

how that the _____ had visited his _____ in giving them bread."

SHE DECIDED TO RETURN HOME TO JERUSALEM.

Ruth 1:7

"Wherefore she went _____ out of the place where she was,

and her two daughters in law with her; and they went

on the way to _____ unto the land of Judah."

She...

NAOMI SERVES AS AN EXAMPLE THAT EVEN AFTER GREAT PAIN AND SORROW, WE CAN RETURN TO WHERE GOD WOULD HAVE US TO BE.

Memorize:
Psalm 51:12
"Restore unto me the joy of thy salvation;
and uphold me with thy free spirit."

Apply:
How have you needed to return unto the Lord in the past?

_____

_____

Ruth 1:20

"...she said unto them, Call me not Naomi..."

SHE WAS WILLING TO BE ALONE.

Ruth 1:8

"And Naomi said unto her two daughters in law, _____, return each

to her mother's house: the LORD deal _____ with you,

as ye have _____ with the dead, and with me."

She urged her daughters to go their own way.

SHE WAS GRIEVED OVER HER SITUATION.

Ruth 1:12-13

"Turn again, my daughters, _____ your way; for I am too _____ to

have an husband... for it grieveth me _____ for your sakes

that the hand of the LORD is _____ out against me."

She went toward Bethlehem joined by only one of her daughters in law.

Ruth 1:14

"And they lifted up their voice, and wept again: and _____ kissed

her mother in law; but _____ clave unto her."

When they got back to Bethlehem,
the people of the city did not even recognize Naomi.

Ruth 1:19

"So they two went until they came to _____. And it came to pass...that

all the city was _____ about them, and they said, Is this Naomi?"

SHE WENT FROM BLISS TO BITTERNESS.

Ruth 1:20
"And she said unto them, Call me not Naomi,

call me _____: for the Almighty hath dealt very _____ with me."

Grief can change us into someone we do not even recognize.
Bitterness had consumed her.

Ruth 1:21

"I went out _____, and the LORD hath brought me home again _____:

why then call ye me Naomi, seeing the _____ hath testified against me,

and the _____ hath afflicted me?"

There are several name changes throughout the holy pages of Scripture.
Many are given of the Lord, but Naomi's was not. She changed it on her own.

SHE KNEW SOMETHING DRASTIC HAD TRANSPIRED WITHIN HER.

God had allowed circumstances to occur due to her disobedience.
Now she felt like a completely different woman
because bitterness had grown inside her.

She...

NAOMI ALSO SERVES AS AN EXAMPLE OF HOW SORROW CAN CHANGE OUR CHARACTER IF WE LET IT.

**However, when we acknowledge it and seek the Lord's help,
He is Faithful to give us just what we need.**

Memorize:
Psalm 34:3-4
*"O magnify the LORD with me, and let us exalt his name together.
I sought the LORD, and he heard me, and delivered me from all my fears."*

Apply:
Has bitterness ever affected you?

_____

Notes

_____

_____

_____

_____

_____

_____

_____

_____

_____

_____

_____

Pharaoh's Daughter

Pharaoh's Daughter

Exodus 2:5

SHE HAD A SPECIFIC TASK,
FOR WHICH THE LORD HAD A GREAT PURPOSE.

Exodus 2:5

"And the daughter of Pharaoh came down to wash herself at the _____; and

her _____ walked along by the river's _____; and when she saw

the ark among the flags, she sent her _____ to fetch it."

SHE SENT HER MAID TO FETCH THE ARK
OUT OF THE RIVER.

Her heart was touched by what was inside.

Exodus 2:6

"And when she had _____ it, she saw the child:

and, behold, the babe wept. And she had _____ on him,

and said, This is _____ of the Hebrews' children."

SHE WAS MOVED WITH COMPASSION.

She desired to meet the needs of the child.
Her maid went and called the child's mother so she could nurse him.

SHE NAMED MOSES.

Exodus 2:10

"And the child _____, and she brought him unto Pharaoh's daughter, and he

became her son. And she _____ his name Moses: and she said,

Because I drew him _____ of the water."

SHE WAS USED BY THE LORD
TO PRESERVE & PROTECT THE LIFE OF MOSES.

**God saw His plan for him long before
he was placed in the ark of bulrushes.**

Moses was the man that God used to lead His people out of bondage.
The faith of Moses is referred to all throughout the entire canon of Scripture.

 *She...*

PHARAOH'S DAUGHTER SERVES AS AN EXAMPLE
THAT GOD ORDERS THE STEPS OF HIS CHILDREN
TO FULFILL HIS PURPOSE.

Memorize:
Psalm 37:23
*"The steps of a good man are ordered by the LORD:
and he delighteth in his way."*

Apply:
When have you been aware of the Lord ordering your steps?

_____

Notes

_____

_____

_____

_____

_____

_____

_____

_____

_____

_____

_____

Ruth

Ruth 1:18

"...she was stedfastly minded..."

SHE WAS A MOABITESS
WHO MARRIED ONE OF NAOMI'S SONS.

Her mother in law begged her and Orpah
to return to Moab after the death of their husbands.

She and Orpah both refused to obey Naomi's request at first,
and desired to go with her back to Bethlehem.

Ruth 1:10

"And they said unto her, Surely we will _____ with thee unto thy people."

Naomi pleaded with them to obey her command.
Orpah decided to do as she requested, but Ruth refused once again.

Ruth 1:14

"And they lifted up their voice, and _____ again:

and Orpah _____ her mother in law; but Ruth _____ unto her."

SHE WAS SERIOUS
ABOUT STAYING WITH NAOMI.

Ruth 1:16-17

"And Ruth said, _____ me not to leave thee, or to return from

_____ after thee: for whither thou goest, I will _____; and where

thou lodgest, I will _____: thy people shall be _____ people,

and thy God my _____: Where thou _____, will I die, and there

will I be _____: the LORD do so to me, and more also,

if ought but _____ part thee and me."

SHE WAS STEDFASTLY MINDED.

Ruth 1:18

"When she saw that she was stedfastly minded

to _____ with her, then she left _____ unto her."

SHE WAS STRONG, COURAGEOUS, BOLD, BRAVE, AND DETERMINED.

If Ruth had given in to Naomi's request, she may have never met Boaz.
**If we give in to the pressure of others,
we are also likely to miss God's will for our lives.**

She...

RUTH SERVES AS AN EXAMPLE THAT WE CAN CHOOSE TO BE STEDFASTLY MINDED ABOUT WHAT GOD HAS GIVEN US TO DO.

Memorize:

Joshua 1:9
*"Have not I commanded thee? Be strong and of a good courage;
be not afraid, neither be thou dismayed: for the LORD thy God
is with thee whithersoever thou goest."*

Apply:

What do you need to be stedfastly minded about?

_____

_____

Ruth 2:3

"...she went, and came, and gleaned in the field..."

SHE WAS DIVINELY DIRECTED BY THE LORD.

Ruth 2:3

"And she went, and came, and gleaned in the field

after the _____: and her hap was to _____ on a part

of the field belonging unto _____, who was of the kindred of Elimelech."

There are no coincidences with God.
It was no accident that God directed her to the field of Boaz.

"she went"
God gave her the faith to go.

"and came"
God directed her steps of where she should go.

"and gleaned"
God provided exactly what she needed, when and where she needed it.

SHE MET BOAZ IN THE FIELD.

She met the man that was of the kindred of her father in law.

Ruth 2:7

"And she said, I pray you, let me glean and _____ after the reapers among

the sheaves: so she came, and hath _____ even from the morning

until now, that she _____ a little in the house."

SHE ASKED TO CONTINUE TO GLEAN IN HIS FIELD.

Boaz encouraged her to stay.
No other field could meet her need.
The field is a picture of the Word of God.

Ruth 2:10

"Then she fell on her face, and _____ herself to the ground,

and said unto him, Why have I found _____ in thine eyes,

that thou shouldest take _____ of me, seeing I am a stranger?"

Everyday we glean from the different things we focus our mind
and spirit on whether it is intentional or not.

Boaz gave Ruth his field to glean from freely.
God has given us His Word and He shares It with us freely.

She...

RUTH ALSO SERVES AS AN EXAMPLE OF HOW IMPORTANT IT IS FOR US TO GLEAN FROM THE WORD OF GOD.

**May we be mindful of where we are spending our time,
and from what field(s) we are gleaning.**

Memorize:
John 5:39
*"Search the scriptures; for in them ye think ye have eternal life:
and they are they which testify of me."*

Apply:
What does it mean to you to glean from the Word of God?

_____

_____

Ruth 2:16

"...she may glean them, and rebuke her not."

SHE FOUND HANDFULS OF PURPOSE.

Ruth 2:15-16

"And when she was _____ up to glean, Boaz commanded his young men,

saying, Let her glean even among the _____, and reproach her not:

And let fall also some of the handfuls of _____ for her,

and _____ them, that she may glean them, and rebuke her not."

Boaz had purposely arranged for the handfuls of purpose to be there...
just for her.

Ruth 2:17-18

"So she gleaned in the field until _____, and beat out that she had gleaned:

and it was about an ephah of _____. And she took it up, and went into the

city: and her mother in law saw what she had _____: and she brought forth,

and gave to her that she had _____ after she was sufficed."

She returned home to Naomi with the reserve of barley,
and the amount sparked the interest of her mother in law.

SHE HELD ABUNDANT GRACE WITHIN HER HANDS.

Naomi asked where she had been to find it.

Ruth 2:19

"...And she shewed her mother in law with _____ she had wrought,

and said, The man's name with whom I _____ to day is Boaz."

SHE HAD FOUND A KINSMAN REDEEMER IN THE FIELD.

Ruth 2:20

"And Naomi said unto her daughter in law, _____ be he of the LORD,

who hath not left off his _____ to the living and to the dead. And Naomi said

unto her, The man is near of _____ unto us, one of our next kinsmen."

She...

RUTH ALSO SERVES AS AN EXAMPLE THAT GOD HAS LEFT "HANDFULS OF PURPOSE" WITHIN HIS WORD THAT HE DESIRES FOR US TO APPLY TO OUR LIVES.

What are you gleaning today?

Memorize:
Psalm 119:18
"Open thou mine eyes,
that I may behold wondrous things out of thy law."

Apply:
What have you recently gleaned from the Word of God?

_____

_____

_____

"...she went down unto the floor..."

Ruth 3:2

"And now is not Boaz of our _____, with whose maidens thou wast?

Behold, he winnoweth _____ to night in the threshingfloor."

Naomi knew that Boaz was working in the threshingfloor,
and what Ruth needed to do.

SHE WAS WILLING.

SHE OBEYED ALL OF HER MOTHER IN LAW'S INSTRUCTIONS.

Ruth 3:6

"And she went down unto the floor,

and _____ according to all that her mother in law _____ her."

SHE HAD FAITH THAT BOAZ WOULD DO WHAT HE COULD.

Ruth 3:7

"And when Boaz had eaten and drunk, and his _____ was merry,

he went to lie _____ at the end of the heap of corn: and she came softly,

and _____ his feet, and laid her down."

Boaz did not know who she was at first.

Ruth 3:9

"And he said, _____ art thou? And she answered, I am Ruth thine handmaid:

spread therefore thy _____ over thine handmaid;

for thou art a _____ kinsman."

He was a near kinsman that could redeem them, and he was willing.

Ruth 3:11

"And now, my daughter, _____ not; I will do to thee

all that thou _____: for all the city of my people doth know

that thou art a _____ woman."

Outside of Proverbs, this is the only reference to a virtuous woman in Scripture.

She was kind and virtuous, and although there was a nearer kinsman,
Boaz was whom God had prepared to be her redeemer.

She...

RUTH ALSO SERVES AS AN EXAMPLE OF HOW
CHRIST IS WILLING TO REDEEM US
IF ONLY WE WILL TRUST IN HIM BY FAITH.

Memorize:
1 Peter 1:18-19
*"Forasmuch as ye know that ye were not redeemed with corruptible things,
as silver and gold, from your vain conversation received by tradition
from your fathers; But with the precious blood of Christ,
as of a lamb without blemish and without spot:"*

Apply:
What does redemption mean to you?

_____

_____

Why do we need a Redeemer?

_____

_____

Ruth 4:13

"...she was his wife..."

SHE WAITED WHILE BOAZ
WENT TO MEET THE NEARER KINSMAN.

The nearer kinsman chose not to redeem both Naomi and Ruth,
but that was no surprise to the Lord.
This simply made it possible for Boaz to do so.

Ruth 4:7-8

"Now this was the manner in former time in Israel

concerning _____ and concerning changing, for to confirm all things;

a man plucked off his _____, and gave it to his neighbour:

and this was a _____ in Israel.

Therefore the kinsman said unto Boaz, _____ it for thee.

So he _____ off his shoe."

That shoe symbolized so much more.

It was a pledge that a transaction had been completed,
and Boaz was now legally able to marry Ruth.

Ruth 4:13

"So Boaz _____ Ruth, and she was his wife:

and when he _____ in unto her,

the LORD _____ her conception, and she _____ a son."

SHE HAD BEEN REDEEMED AND RESTORED.
SHE BARE A SON SOON AFTER THEIR MARRIAGE.

Ruth 4:14-15

"And the women said unto Naomi, _____ be the LORD, which hath

not left thee this day _____ a kinsman, that his name

may be _____ in Israel. And he shall be unto thee

a _____ of thy life, and a _____ of thine old age:

for thy daughter in law, which _____ thee,

which is better to thee than seven sons, hath _____ him."

She was given a legacy of redemption.

That baby would be the grandfather of King David of Israel.

And fourteen generations after him,
Jesus Christ would be born of the same lineage.

Ruth also serves as an example of the beautiful picture of redemption that Christ has provided us.

Memorize:

Ephesians 1:7
*"In whom we have redemption through his blood,
the forgiveness of sins, according to the riches of his grace;"*

Apply:

What was the name of Ruth & Boaz's son? Matthew 1:5

_____

Notes

_____

_____

_____

_____

_____

_____

_____

_____

_____

_____

Sapphira

Acts 5:10

"...she down straightway at his feet..."

SHE AND HER HUSBAND
WERE DELIBERATELY WICKED.

Acts 5:1-2

"But a certain man named _____, with Sapphira his wife,

_____ a possession, And kept back part of the _____,

his wife also being privy to it, and brought a certain _____,

and laid it at the apostles' feet."

She and her husband deceived people
by agreeing together to surrender a part
as if they had surrendered all.

Acts 5:3

"But Peter said, Ananias, why hath Satan filled thine _____ to lie to the

Holy Ghost, and to _____ back part of the price of the land?"

Acts 5:4

"...thou hast not lied unto _____, but unto _____."

Ananias lied to God and suffered the consequences.

Acts 5:5

"And Ananias hearing these words _____ down, and gave up the ghost:

and great _____ came on all them that heard these things."

Peter also rebuked her for agreeing together
with her husband to tempt the Spirit of the Lord
about their sold possession.

SHE RECEIVED GOD'S JUDGMENT FOR HER DECEITFULNESS.

Acts 5:10

"Then fell she down straightway at his feet, and _____ up the ghost:

and the young men came in, and found her _____, and,

carrying her forth, _____ her by her husband."

Their deception cost both of them their lives.

The punishment they received brought great fear
upon all who heard what the Lord had done.

Acts 5:11

"And great fear came upon all the _____, and upon

as many as _____ these things."

She...

SAPPHIRA SERVES AS AN EXAMPLE OF HOW DANGEROUS IT IS FOR US TO PORTRAY TO BE SOMETHING WE ARE NOT.

Memorize:
Jeremiah 17:9
"The heart is deceitful above all things, and desperately wicked: who can know it?"

Apply:
Give another example of someone who deceived people by their actions:

_____

_____

_____

Notes

_____

_____

_____

_____

_____

_____

_____

_____

_____

_____

_____

The True Harlot Mother

The True Harlot Mother

1 Kings 3:27

> **"...she is the mother thereof."**

SHE WAS ONE OF TWO WOMEN WHO BOTH CLAIMED TO BE THE MOTHER OF THE SAME CHILD.

1 Kings 3:16

"Then came there two women, that were _____, unto the king,

and stood before him."

They both appeared before King Solomon
so that he could wisely judge who was the true mother.

1 Kings 3:19-20

"And this woman's child _____ in the night; because she overlaid it. And she

arose at midnight, and _____ my son from beside me, while thine handmaid

slept, and laid it in her bosom, and laid her dead _____ in my bosom."

SHE SPOKE THE TRUTH.

She spoke of her need to be vindicated as the mother of the child.

1 Kings 3:21

"And when I rose in the _____ to give my child suck,

behold, it was _____: but when I had considered it in the morning,

behold, it was _____ my son, which I did bear."

**Solomon wisely suggested that the child be cut in half,
in order to reveal who was really the true mother.**

SHE WAS WILLING TO LOSE HER CHILD IN ORDER TO SAVE HIS LIFE.

1 Kings 3:26

"Then spake the woman whose the _____ child was unto the king, for her

bowels yearned upon her son, and she said, O my lord, _____ her the living

child, and in _____ wise slay it. But the other said,

Let it be neither mine nor thine, but _____ it."

King Solomon in his wisdom knew
that she would sacrifice her own desires in order to save her son.

1 Kings 3:27

"Then the king answered and said, Give her the living _____, and

in no _____ slay it: she is the mother thereof."

She...

THE TRUE HARLOT MOTHER SERVES AS

AN EXAMPLE THAT WE MUST BE WILLING

TO SUFFER GREAT LOSS IN ORDER

TO BE USED FOR GOD'S GLORY.

Memorize:
Matthew 10:39
"He that findeth his life shall lose it:
and he that loseth his life for my sake shall find it."

Apply:
Give another example of someone willing to suffer great loss for God's glory:

_____

_____

_____

Notes

_____

_____

_____

_____

_____

_____

_____

_____

_____

_____

_____

The Widow With Two Mites

Read: Mark 12:41-44
Luke 21:1-4

The Widow With Two Mites

Mark 12:42

"...she threw in two mites..."

SHE DID NOT HAVE WHAT SEEMED LIKE MUCH TO GIVE.

Mark 12:42

"And there came a certain _____ widow,

and she threw in two mites,

which _____ a farthing."

SHE WAS AMONG THE RICH.

Luke 21:1-2

"And he looked up, and saw the rich _____ casting

their _____ into the treasury. And he saw also

a _____ poor widow casting in thither two mites."

While the rich gave of their abundance, she gave of her deficiency.

Luke 21:3-4

"And he said, Of a _____ I say unto you, that this poor widow hath cast in

_____ than they all: For all these have of their _____ cast

in unto the offerings of God: but she of her _____ hath cast

in all the living that she had."

SHE HELD NOTHING BACK.

Her gift was a sacrifice.
She gave all that she could possibly give.

SHE CAST IN ALL THE LIVING SHE HAD.

She surrendered all she had to Him.

May we choose to willingly give all we have
so that He would be glorified.

Little is much when God is in it!

The Widow With Two Mites serves as an example of how any sacrifice for Christ does not go unnoticed by Him.

Memorize:

Romans 12:1
*"I beseech you therefore, brethren, by the mercies of God,
that ye present your bodies a living sacrifice,
holy, acceptable unto God, which is your reasonable service."*

Apply:

What has this widow taught you?

_____

_____

_____

_____

Notes

_____

_____

_____

_____

_____

_____

_____

_____

_____

_____

_____

The Woman With An Issue Of Blood

The Woman With An Issue Of Blood

Luke 8:47

"...she had touched him..."

SHE WAS DESPERATE.

Mark 5:25-26

"And a certain woman, which had an issue of blood _____ years,

And had _____ many things of many physicians,

and had _____ all that she had, and was _____ bettered,

but rather _____ worse,"

SHE HAD SPENT ALL SHE HAD LOOKING FOR A CURE.

Luke 8:43

"And a woman having an issue of blood

twelve _____, which had spent all her living

upon physicians, _____ could be healed of any,"

SHE HAD TRIED EVERYTHING, EXCEPT HIM.

SHE BELIEVED HE COULD HEAL HER.

Matthew 9:20

"And, behold, a woman, which was _____ with

an issue of blood twelve years, came _____ him,

and touched the _____ of his garment:

For she said within herself, If I may but _____ his garment,

I _____ be whole."

SHE BELIEVED ALL SHE HAD TO DO WAS TOUCH THE HEM OF HIS GARMENT.

Luke 8:47

"And when the woman saw that she was not _____, she came trembling, and falling down before him, she _____ unto him before all the people for what cause she had touched him, and how she was _____ immediately."

Her single act of great faith resulted in the healing that she needed.

She...

THE WOMAN WITH AN ISSUE OF BLOOD SERVES AS AN EXAMPLE THAT ONE TOUCH OF JESUS CAN MAKE A DIFFERENCE.

Memorize:

Hebrews 11:6
*"But without faith it is impossible to please him:
for he that cometh to God must believe that he is,
and that he is a rewarder of them that diligently seek him."*

Apply:

What was so special about the garment Jesus was wearing?

_____

_____

_____

The Woman With An Issue Of Blood

Mark 5:27

"...she had heard of Jesus..."

SHE HAD HEARD THAT HE HAD HEALED MANY PEOPLE OF THEIR INFIRMITIES.

Mark 5:27

"When she had heard of Jesus, came in the _____ behind,

and _____ his garment."

Who told her about Him?

The Scriptures do not tell us
specifically who told this woman of Jesus,
but someone did.

That person told her of the Solution to her twelve-year long problem.

SHE MET THE ANSWER TO HER NEED.

Luke 8:44

"Came behind him, and touched the _____ of his garment:

and _____ her issue of blood stanched."

SHE HAD FAITH IN HIM.

Luke 8:46

"And Jesus said, _____ hath touched me:

for I perceive that virtue is gone _____ of me."

Mark 5:28

"For she said, If I may touch but his _____, I shall be whole."

SHE WAS HEALED BECAUSE SOMEONE TOLD HER OF HIM.

Mark 5:34

"And he said unto her, Daughter, thy _____ hath made thee whole;

go in _____, and be _____ of thy plague."

SHE BROUGHT OTHERS TO JESUS THROUGH HER TESTIMONY.

Matthew 14:36

"And besought him that they might only touch the _____ of his garment:

and as _____ as touched were made perfectly whole."

They must have heard that one touch of the hem of His garment had brought her healing; and had faith that if He could heal her, He could heal them too.

She...

THE WOMAN WITH AN ISSUE OF BLOOD
ALSO SERVES AS AN EXAMPLE OF THE
IMPORTANCE OF TELLING OTHERS ABOUT JESUS.

Someone told you of your need for Jesus.
Where would you be
if they chose not to share the Good News with you?

Tell someone about Jesus today.

Memorize:
Romans 1:16
"For I am not ashamed of the gospel of Christ:
for it is the power of God unto salvation to every one that believeth;
to the Jew first, and also to the Greek."

Apply:
Who told you about Jesus? Thank them today.

Notes

_____

_____

_____

_____

_____

_____

_____

_____

_____

_____

_____

Be A Woman Of The Bible

Be A Woman Of The Bible

Did you know that there are three distinct ways to understand the Bible?

READ
Deuteronomy 17:19

SEARCH
John 5:39

STUDY
2 Timothy 2:15

You have studied the lives of 12 Women of the Bible.
Their names or testimonies are recorded on the pages of the Word of God for specific purposes. The characteristics of their lives are examples of the many things you can choose to apply to your life.

Although your name is not printed in the canon of the Scriptures, you can still be known as a Woman of the Bible by purposing yourself to use the qualities of their lives to affect how you walk with the Lord.

The Book of James describes two different choices you have
in your response to what you find in the Word of God.

James 1:22-25
*"But be ye doers of the word, and not hearers only, deceiving your own selves.
For if any be a hearer of the word, and not a doer, he is like unto a man beholding his natural face in a glass: For he beholdeth himself, and goeth his way,
and straightway forgetteth what manner of man he was.
But whoso looketh into the perfect law of liberty, and continueth therein, he being not a forgetful hearer, but a doer of the work, this man shall be blessed in his deed."*

LIVE OUT WHAT YOU KNOW.

If you are to be known as a woman who follows Biblical Truth,
you have to live out what you know.
"doers of the word, and not hearers only"

There is a difference between what you know and what you believe.

Many people who call themselves "Christians" know Biblical Truth.
They know that Jesus Christ was the Son of God.
They know that Jesus died on the cross.

They even know that He died on the cross of their sins.
They know a lot of things...but have they believed on Him?

**There is a difference in knowing something,
and actually believing, or placing your faith in it.**

Many have heard the phrase that "people can be 18 inches away from Heaven". The principle found here is so true.

Many know that Abraham Lincoln was the 16th President of the United States of America. Many even know that he famously spoke the Emancipation Proclamation, and that he led the abolishment of slavery.

They have never met him, yet they know many things about him.

There are many people that know countless facts about Who Jesus is, yet they have not placed their faith and trust in what He did on the cross for them.

That is the difference.

LIVE OUT WHAT YOU BELIEVE.

The same principle applies to the women you have studied throughout this book. You can know everything about their lives, so much so that you could clear the "Women of the Bible" column on the Jeopardy board, but if you do not apply what you know to your life it simply ends with knowledge.

You can know many many things found within the pages of God's Word, but if you only hear them without being a doer of those Truths, the Book of James clearly says that you are deceiving yourself.

Be A Woman Of The Bible

References

References

ANNA
"Favor or Grace"

LUKE 2:36-38

EVE
"Mother of All Living"

GENESIS 2 & 3

2 CORINTHIANS 11:3; 1 TIMOTHY 2:13

HANNAH
"Gracious"

1 SAMUEL 1, 2:1-26

JOCHEBED
"Glory of Jehovah"

EXODUS 1, 2:1-11, 6:20

NUMBERS 26:59; HEBREWS 11:23

MARY MAGDALENE
"Bitter Tower or Castle"

MATTHEW 27:56, 61, 28:1

MARK 15:40-47, 16:1-19

LUKE 8:2, 24:10

JOHN 19:25, 20:1-18

NAOMI
"My Joy, My Bliss"

RUTH 1-4

Pharaoh's Daughter
Exodus 2:5-10
Acts 7:21; Hebrews 11:24

Ruth
"Female Friend / Friendship"
Ruth 1-4
Matthew 1:5

Sapphira
"Beautiful or Pleasant"
Acts 5:1-11

The True Harlot Mother
1 Kings 3

The Widow With Two Mites
Mark 12:41-44
Luke 21:1-4

The Woman With An Issue Of Blood
Matthew 9:20-22
Mark 5:25-34
Luke 8:43-48

About Us

About Us

*"Delight thyself also in the LORD;
and he shall give thee the desires of thine heart."*
Psalm 37:4

From this verse comes the inspiration behind the name of this ministry. It is a reminder that if we delight ourselves in Him, He promises to give us desires according to His will for our lives.

In 2012, the desire for a design ministry began. The Lord has since opened door after door to allow that desire to become a reality...*"Commit thy way unto the LORD; trust also in him; and he shall bring it to pass."* Psalm 37:5

Delight Thyself Design Ministries began as a media ministry at Teays Valley Baptist Church of Hurricane, WV. Then Lord directed us toward reaching people with the printed Word of the Gospel. A tract ministry was born, and has since continued to grow as the Lord leads. In 2014, we began shipping tracts to missionaries across the world with little or no material with which to reach their field. **Please pray with us** that the Lord will continue to provide resources to print the tracts the missionaries are requesting.

We ship tracts free of charge to anyone willing to distribute the printed Word of the Gospel of Jesus Christ. Contact us if you would like to receive a sample pack or box to distribute.

Gospel tracts customized with a church's contact information are a great way to spread the Gospel and allow others to contact your ministry. We also design custom material for Independent Baptist Churches, which helps fund the printing and distribution of Gospel tracts which are sent across the world.

We are so thankful for those whom the Lord has provided to support this ministry on a monthly basis or through one time donations. If it were not for the Lord using these generous people, this ministry simply could not exist today. We claim Philippians 4:17 for this method of support, *"Not because I desire a gift: but I desire fruit that may abound to your account."*

If you would like to receive ministry updates, follow us on social media or send us your email address to receive our newsletters.

Delight Thyself
DESIGN MINISTRIES

delightthyself.com

What Can One Tract Do?

One tract was sitting in the office of the home of a young man named, Hudson. When he found it, he read over it and the phrase "the finished work of Christ" began to work on his heart about his need for salvation. He then surrendered his life to Christ, and was burdened for the people of China. This man was who we now know as Hudson Taylor, the missionary who brought the Good News of the Gospel to China.

One tract was given by a friend to a man named Joe. Over the next several months, the Lord used that tract to put him under conviction, cause him to go to church and walk the aisle to trust Christ as His Saviour. When he got up, he saw his pregnant wife beside him. She had also came forward by faith to accept Christ. This is the testimony of the parents of the founder of this ministry. One tract led to their salvation, a Christian heritage, and the start of this ministry. Without God using a man to give that one tract, this ministry would not exist today.

One tract has now yielded nearly 2,000,000 tracts to date being sent all across the world, and only heaven will reveal the fruit that remains. To God be the glory, for great things only He hath done.

Isaiah 55:11
"So shall my word be that goeth forth out of my mouth:
it shall not return unto me void,
but it shall accomplish that which I please,
and it shall prosper in the thing whereto I sent it."

Will you allow God to use you
to spread the printed Word of the Gospel?

Visit delightthyself.com for more resources.

ONE TRACT
CAN
MAKE A
DIFFERENCE

The Bible Way To Heaven

"Jesus saith unto him, I am the way, the truth, and the life;
no man cometh unto the Father, but by me."
John 14:6

We Are All Sinners.
"For all have sinned, and come short of the glory of God."
Romans 3:23

We Were Sent A Saviour.
"But God commendeth his love toward us, in that,
while we were yet sinners, Christ died for us."
Romans 5:8

We Were Supplied A Gift.
"For the wages of sin is death;
but the gift of God is eternal life through Jesus Christ our Lord."
Romans 6:23

We Can Simply Confess & Call.
"That if thou shalt confess with thy mouth the Lord Jesus,
and shalt believe in thine heart that God
hath raised him from the dead, thou shalt be saved.
For whosoever shall call upon the name of the Lord shall be saved."
Romans 10:9,13

It's that simple.

The Bible says... **Whosoever.**
Once you see yourself as a sinner, if you will simply *"call upon the name of the Lord"*, you can be saved from spending eternity in the Lake of Fire separated from God. You may say..."It's not for me." or "I'll never be good enough.", but God said... **Whosoever.**

God is not willing that any should perish.
That includes you.

If you have trusted Christ as your Saviour,
or would like more information, please contact us.

delightthyself.com

CPSIA information can be obtained
at www.ICGtesting.com
Printed in the USA
JSHW010322250520
5860JS00002B/4

9 780999 517567